As World War II loomed, the Royal the Hawker Aircraft Company to produce a two-seat fighter. The result was the Hawker Hotspur, which first flew in 1938, achieving the speed of 316 m.p.h. Despite this success, the R.A.F. decided to go for a single-seater, and the Hurricane replaced the Hotspur on the assembly lines.

Five ships of the Royal Navy have proudly borne the name H.M.S. Hotspur. The first was launched in 1810, the latest being a "Hero" Class destroyer built in 1936. This destroyer fought in the Battle of Narvik Fiord, escorted convoys of supply ships to the besieged port of Tobruk and accompanied the D-Day landings. Despite frequent shell and bomb damage, H.M.S. Hotspur was never put out of action, and fought throughout World War II, from the first day to the last.

PRICE
85p

THE HOTSPUR

BOOK FOR BOYS 1977

A FEAST OF SUPER STORIES

CONTENTS

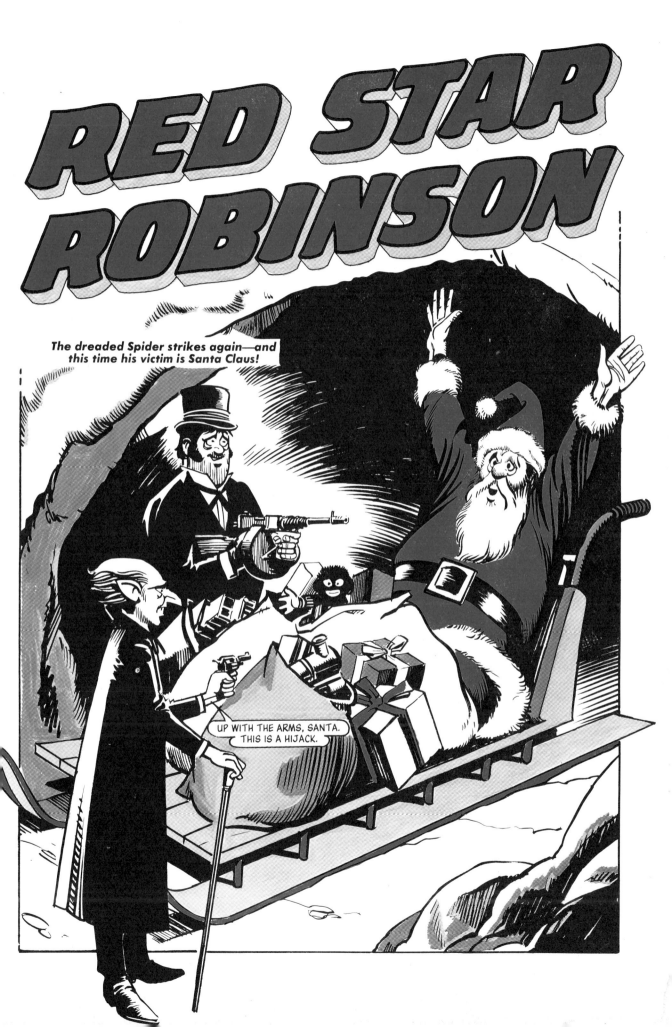

AN unfortunate incident disturbed the peace of Tom Robinson and Mr Syrius Thrice, the cultured robot, those tireless helpers of The Watcher in that mysterious being's unceasing war on crime. Tom and Mr Thrice had returned to Earth for a Christmas break after service as Special Agents of the Galactic Police Federation.

A CALL ON THE VIDEO, MR THRICE. YOU'D BETTER STOP STIRRING THE CHRISTMAS PUDDING.

The call was from The Watcher.

GENTLEMEN, I REGRET TO INTRUDE UPON YOUR FESTIVE ARRANGEMENTS, BUT THE SPIDER HAS ESCAPED FROM PARKMOOR MAXIMUM SECURITY PRISON. IT WOULD APPEAR THAT THIS SINISTER MASTERMIND OF CRIME DELUDED THE AUTHORITIES BY SEEMING TO ACCEPT PRISON LIFE. HE ORGANISED VARIOUS ACTIVITIES FOR THE OTHER INMATES...

THEIR ESCAPE VEHICLE HAS BEEN FOUND LESS THAN TWENTY MILES FROM THE PRISON—ON THE OUTSKIRTS OF YARETON NEW PORT, GENTLEMEN. I WOULD SUGGEST THAT AS THE STARTING POINT FOR YOUR INVESTIGATION.

WE SHALL SET OFF IMMEDIATELY IN THE RED STAR LIMOUSINE, SIR.

...INCLUDING A PHOTOGRAPHY CLUB. BUT THIS WAS JUST PART OF AN ESCAPE PLAN FOR THE SPIDER AND HIS MINION.

A swift jet hop brought Tom and Mr Thrice over Yareton.

THERE IS THE VEHICLE. BUT HOW CAN WE SEARCH FOR CLUES WHILE IT IS WATCHED BY POLICE OFFICERS?

THERE IS A WAY, MASTER TOM. FIRST I SHALL LAND IN ANOTHER PART OF THE BREAKER'S YARD.

NOW WE CAN INVESTIGATE FROM LONG RANGE BY MEANS OF MY REMOTE-CONTROL SCANNER DISGUISED AS A COMMON CRAB.

OH, VERY CLEVER, MR THRICE.

The robot guided his electronic crab into the guarded vehicle.

NOT A CLUE SO FAR, MR THRICE. THE POLICE HAVE PROBABLY ALREADY GONE OVER THE VEHICLE.

STILL, MASTER TOM, I SUGGEST WE COMPLETE THE SEARCH.

WHAT'S THAT, MR THRICE?

A PIECE OF PAPER, MASTER TOM, CARELESSLY DROPPED AND TRODDEN UNDERFOOT. IT COULD BE IMPORTANT—

The crab brought them the crumpled paper.

THIS CAN'T BE ANYTHING TO DO WITH THE SPIDER, MR THRICE. CHRISTMAS SHOPPING, AND TOYLAND—

GOSLING AND GRIPP

COME TO THE SUPER STORE WITH A HEART FOR YOUR CHRISTMAS SHOPPING. VISIT FATHER CHRISTMAS IN TOYLAND AND

MASTER TOM, WE MUST TREAT THIS ADVERTISEMENT AS A CLUE, UNTIL IT CAN BE ELIMINATED.

GOLDBLOCKS

WE'RE ALMOST AT GOSLING AND GRIPP'S SUPERSTORE, MASTER TOM. I MUST FIND A PARKING PLACE.

In the superstore.

TOY LAND

THIS WAY, MISTER THRICE.

The arrival of the Red Star pair had been observed on the security closed circuit television system.

LOOK, SPIDER—IT'S THEM! THE TIN GEEZER AND THAT NOSEY KID.

SO—ONCE AGAIN THOSE TWO THINK TO INTERFERE WITH MY PLANS. IT SHALL NOT BE!

THAT WOULD APPEAR TO BE OUR DESTINATION.

SANTA'S GROTTO

WHY DID YOU GIVE ME THIS ROTTEN DRUM? I WANTED A BOPPER-WHOPPER DEATH RAY GUN.

PUSH ORF OR YOU'LL GET ME 'AND ACROSS YER EAR 'OLE.

WITH THE COMPLIMENTS OF OLD DADDY CHRISTMAS, YOUNG FELLER— A LAUGHING JACK-IN-A-BOX. OPEN THE LID AND YOU GETS A SURPRISE.

OH-ER, THANKS. A MERRY CHRISTMAS TO YOU, SIR.

NOTHING SUSPICIOUS SO FAR, MR THRICE. I'M BECOMING CONVINCED THAT ADVERT WAS A FALSE LEAD.

IT SEEMS SO, MASTER TOM. I SUGGEST WE RETURN TO THE LIMOUSINE AND REPORT TO THE WATCHER.

Outside the superstore.

IS THIS YOUR VEHICLE, SIR? YOU'LL HAVE TO MOVE IT OFF THESE DOUBLE YELLOW LINES.

AT ONCE, WARDEN.

REPORT FROM COMPUTER! AN EXPLOSIVE DEVICE IN UNSTABLE CONDITION HAS JUST BEEN BROUGHT ABOARD.

YOUR PARCEL, MASTER TOM! WE MUST CONVEY IT INSTANTLY FROM THESE CROWDED STREETS.

The Red Star limousine was swiftly unparked—upwards!

I SUGGEST THE HARBOUR, MASTER TOM.

Seconds later, an explosion shook the city.

HEH! HEH! THAT'S DEALT WITH THOSE TWO MEDDLING FOOLS.

Meanwhile, above the harbour.

PHEW! WE DUMPED THAT JUST IN TIME, MR THRICE. NOW WE'LL MAKE OUR REPORT TO THE WATCHER.

9

I'VE JUST BEEN GIVEN AN EXPLOSIVE CHRISTMAS PRESENT, SIR. SUCH A DEED IS SO TYPICAL OF THE SPIDER THAT MR THRICE AND I WILL INVESTIGATE THE SUPERSTORE, AFTER IT HAS CLOSED.

I WISH YOU SUCCESS.

Midnight. The Red Star limousine landed on the roof of Gosling and Gripp.

WE SHOULD BE ABLE TO ENTER BY WAY OF THAT LIFT-HEAD STRUCTURE, MASTER TOM.

ONE MOMENT, MASTER TOM. MY AUDIO SENSORS DETECT UNUSUAL SOUNDS AT THE REAR OF THE BUILDING.

THE SPIDER IN A BUCKET! HE MUST BE USING THE SUPERSTORE TO GAIN ACCESS TO THAT OTHER BUILDING.

THAT OTHER PROPERTY BELONGS TO ROSENGRIT, THE JEWELLERS. WE PARKED IN FRONT OF IT.

The Red Star crime fighters hurried downstairs.

MR THRICE—LISTEN! THAT CUPBOARD!

GOOD GRIEF! IT'S A POOR OLD MAN.

I'M FATHER CHRISTMAS. TWO FUNNY-LOOKING BLOKES SAID THEY WERE TAKING OVER, AND TIED ME UP.

10 *Leaving the old gentleman, the Red Star pair headed for Toyland. But—*

IT'S THEM TWO AGAIN, SPIDER. THEY'RE STILL ALIVE.

WHAT? WELL, DON'T JUST STAND THERE, KRAGWORT—DO SOMETHING ABOUT THEM.

So—

TAKE COVER, MASTER TOM. WE ARE AMBUSHED.

SPORTS GOODS

THE VILLAIN HAS US PINNED DOWN, MASTER TOM. I SUGGEST WE RETURN HIS FIRE WITH YONDER AUTOMATIC TENNIS-SERVER.

OUCH! HOLD ON—ERK!

GOOD SHOOTING, MR THRICE. HE'S HEADING FOR THE MAGIC GROTTO.

THE END

15

Nick Jolly

A FINE MORNING, BESS—FOR A HOLD-UP. A HARD-WORKING HIGHWAYMAN MUST EARN A PENNY OR TWO.

NICK JOLLY, a dare-devil 18th century highwayman, had been carried into the 20th century by an amazing time-ray. His sword had been electrified and the ray had transformed his trusty mare, Bess, into an incredible jet-propelled horse of steel.

Far from the action was the owner and maker of the uncanny toy.

RETURN, MY LITTLE ONE. I'LL COME OUT TO MEET YOU. MY CRIMINAL TOYS ARE SUPERIOR TO THE DULL WITS OF THE POLICE.

GREEN PARK STATION

COME, LITTLE ONE! INTO MY CASE! HEH-HEH! THERE WILL BE MANY MORE RAIDS USING YOU AND YOUR FRIENDS.

But then—

MY TRUSTY BESS TRACKED THE MANIKIN WELL.

GREETINGS, SIR! I ASK TO SEE WHAT YOU HAVE IN YOUR CASE.

THE ACCURSED FLYING HIGHWAYMAN!

Nick tripped on a real toy.

HELP! ROBBERY! HE'S AFTER MY BAG. POLICE!

OOOOOGH! PLAGUE ON'T!

As Nick sprawled, stunned—

HOLD NICK! HE'S WANTED FOR QUESTIONING ABOUT A JEWEL ROBBERY.

SORRY, NICK! IT'S HARD TO THINK OF YOU AS A BAG-SNATCHER. BUT YOU HAVE SOME EXPLAINING TO DO.

CAUGHT BY THE BOW STREET RUNNERS! HERE'S A PRETTY KETTLE OF FISH.

NO MATTER—BESS IS STILL FREE. 'TIS CERTAIN SHE'LL STAY CLOSE. NO HIGH-WAYMAN EVER HAD A MORE INCREDIBLE STEED.

The toymaker fell against his control panel, and—

AAAAAAAH! A SHORT-CIRCUIT...

I' FAITH! TRAPPED BY HIS OWN CONTRAPTIONS.

HELP! HELP! EVERYTHING'S WRECKED.

The commotion had been heard.

BOW STREET RUNNERS! 'TIS NO PLACE FOR US, BESS! GREETINGS, LAW FRIENDS, YOU'LL FIND A VILLAIN INSIDE!

NICK'S HOUSE-BREAKING NOW!

HERE ARE THE BAUBLES YOU LOST. I RELIEVED THE MANIKIN'S MASTER OF A FEW SILVER COINS FOR MYSELF.

THE STOLEN DIAMONDS! NICK'S THE BEST CROOK-CATCHER THERE IS!

THE END

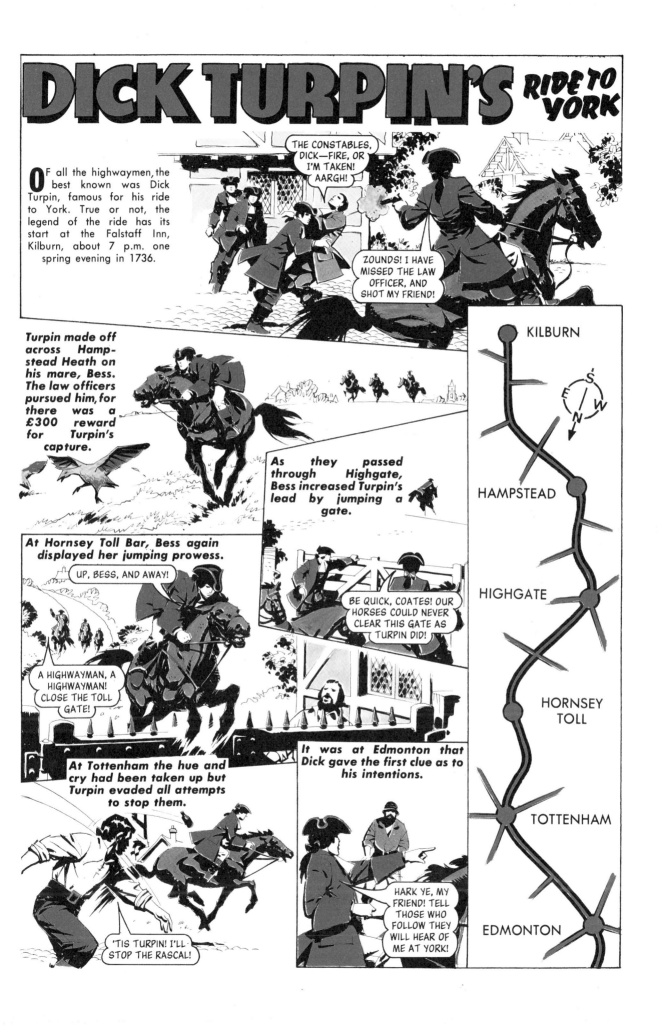

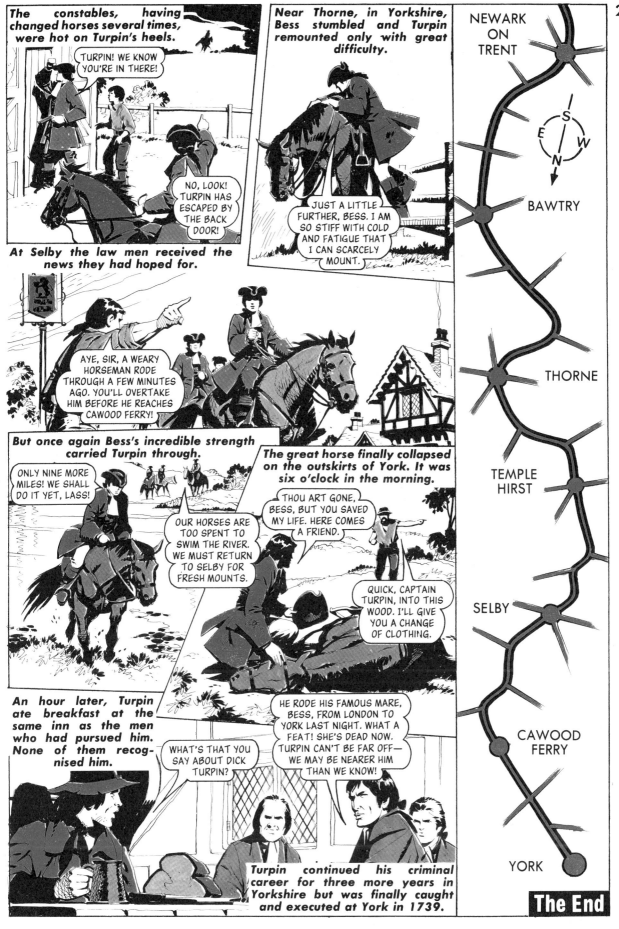

The constables, having changed horses several times, were hot on Turpin's heels.

TURPIN! WE KNOW YOU'RE IN THERE!

NO, LOOK! TURPIN HAS ESCAPED BY THE BACK DOOR!

Near Thorne, in Yorkshire, Bess stumbled and Turpin remounted only with great difficulty.

JUST A LITTLE FURTHER, BESS. I AM SO STIFF WITH COLD AND FATIGUE THAT I CAN SCARCELY MOUNT.

At Selby the law men received the news they had hoped for.

AYE, SIR, A WEARY HORSEMAN RODE THROUGH A FEW MINUTES AGO. YOU'LL OVERTAKE HIM BEFORE HE REACHES CAWOOD FERRY!

But once again Bess's incredible strength carried Turpin through.

ONLY NINE MORE MILES! WE SHALL DO IT YET, LASS!

OUR HORSES ARE TOO SPENT TO SWIM THE RIVER. WE MUST RETURN TO SELBY FOR FRESH MOUNTS.

The great horse finally collapsed on the outskirts of York. It was six o'clock in the morning.

THOU ART GONE, BESS, BUT YOU SAVED MY LIFE. HERE COMES A FRIEND.

QUICK, CAPTAIN TURPIN, INTO THIS WOOD. I'LL GIVE YOU A CHANGE OF CLOTHING.

An hour later, Turpin ate breakfast at the same inn as the men who had pursued him. None of them recognised him.

WHAT'S THAT YOU SAY ABOUT DICK TURPIN?

HE RODE HIS FAMOUS MARE, BESS, FROM LONDON TO YORK LAST NIGHT. WHAT A FEAT! SHE'S DEAD NOW. TURPIN CAN'T BE FAR OFF— WE MAY BE NEARER HIM THAN WE KNOW!

Turpin continued his criminal career for three more years in Yorkshire but was finally caught and executed at York in 1739.

NEWARK ON TRENT

S

E

W

N

BAWTRY

THORNE

TEMPLE HIRST

SELBY

CAWOOD FERRY

YORK

The End

BARNACLE BILLY

YOUNG Billy Perkins was the new deck-boy aboard the steam-tug, Titan. But Billy hadn't found his sea-legs yet—

OOO-ER!

YOUNG BILLY'S A RIGHT LAND-LUBBER! HE KEEPS FORGETTIN' TO MOVE WITH THE ROLL OF THE SHIP.

HERE, BILLY. SWAB DOWN THE DECKS.

WHERE DO I GET THE WATER FROM—OH, I FORGOT THERE'S PLENTY OF IT OVER THE SIDE!

BILLY! DON'T THROW THE BUCKET OUT LIKE THAT— YOU'LL GO—

The two men moved outside, and—

WHASSAT?

A BLOOMIN' ROCKET!

Meanwhile.

THAT'S THE SIGNAL TO THE TITAN AND THIS ROPE SHOULD SCUPPER THEIR GETAWAY.

Aboard the Titan.

WHAT'S HAPPENING!

LOOTERS ON THE CRUISER. SEE, IN THE SEARCH LIGHT BEAM!

THEY'LL GET CLEAN AWAY! THE OLD TITAN WILL NEVER CATCH THEM.

SHE WON'T HAVE TO, CHIPPY. JUST WATCH—

I TIED A ROPE ROUND THEIR PROPELLER AND MADE IT FAST TO THE CRUISER! I DIDN'T THINK THEY'D GET FAR!

YEOW!

GET READY WITH THE BOAT HOOK, AND PICK OUT THOSE SACKS OF VALUABLES TOO!

THAT'S THEM ALL, CAP'N. IT'S YOUNG BILLY WE'VE GOT TO THANK FOR THIS.

AYE, I'LL HAVE A WORD WITH HIM IN THE MORNING. IT WAS QUICK THINKING WHAT HE DID.

Next morning.

WELL DONE, BILLY, HOW'D YOU DO IT, LAD?

I TIED A TRIPWIRE TO THE STRINGS THAT FIRE THE FLARES, CAP'N! WHEN THEY SET IT OFF THEY PANICKED AND MADE FOR THE BOAT!

Meanwhile on the cruiser.

AAGH! I'VE TRIPPED!

IT'S SET OFF THE ROCKET IN THE DIRECTION OF THE TITAN.

BLISTERING BARNACLES! WE'RE UNDER ATTACK!

OH, NO! SOMEONE'S TRIGGERED OFF THE OTHER ROCKET!

And so Billy got a rocketing!

SPUD-BASHING—AND WHEN YOU'RE FINISHED THE DECK NEEDS ANOTHER SWABBING. I'LL GIVE YOU FIREWORKS, MY LAD!

The End

37

SMART SMUGGLERS

SCHOOL FOR SMUGGLERS—A school in Paris charged £10 a lesson. Expensive? Not really. Its pupils were taught how to smuggle goods past the customs.

GOLDEN CAR—To smuggle gold into Pakistan, smugglers turned the gold into mudguards. They painted the mudguards and drove the car over the border.

WHAT A CARRY ON—A man smuggled his son out of a country by carrying him over 900 miles—in a suitcase!

BRINGING HOME THE BACON—In the days when there was a duty on pigs, a woman carried one into Austria each day—dressed as a baby!

OINK

GHOST RIDERS—Cornish smugglers used to paint their wagons white and muffle their horses' hooves to scare off unwelcome visitors.

GIVEAWAY — Smugglers often give themselves away with nervous habits—like smoking too much.

DOPEY COD—A fishmonger got a shock when he cut open a cod. Inside was a bottle of dope, one of a consignment which had gone astray!

FOOTLOOSE—A man tried to smuggle jewels in a heavily bandaged foot. He was spotted when he put his weight on it by mistake!

SMOOTH AS SILK—A silk smuggler was given away when a customs man admired silk round a child's doll. "That's nothing to what my mum has round her," replied the child.

DEAD BEAT—London police became suspicious when a funeral left the same house three weeks in succession. The coffin contained dope.

WATCH IT—Smugglers are up to all sorts of tricks in their efforts to fool the Customs. Even babies bottles have been used!

IN A HOLE—A smuggler with left-handed golf clubs was caught—because he signed his name with his right hand.

AND SOME NOT SO SMART

THE TEAM OF THE DRAGON

SULO, Clenton Orient's player from the Dragon Monastery in the Himalayas, made an amazing clearance in Orient's Charity Cup game against Dale United.

43

ERNEST RUTHERFORD

THE MAN WHO SPLIT THE ATOM

A New Zealander, Ernest Rutherford was born at Nelson in 1871.

As a boy on his father's farm, he showed his resourcefulness when sent to fetch a cow and gather firewood He tied the wood to the cow's tail. The dodge worked well until the wood got stuck in a narrow gate.

Rutherford entered Christchurch University on a scholarship at 17. Working in a draughty cellar used as a cloakroom, he designed and set up a successful apparatus for the detection of electro-magnetic waves.

Already famous but with little money, Rutherford took up school teaching. He was not a success, finding it impossible to keep control of a class.

Then came an offer of a scholarship to Cambridge. Rutherford eagerly accepted and, under Professor J.J. Thomson, used X-rays and the cathode-ray tube to study the mysterious particles known as electrons.

From this developed Rutherford's understanding of the structure of the atom. By 1907, when he became Director of Manchester University Laboratory, he had built a model to show that structure. The next year he received the Nobel Prize for Chemistry.

In World War I Rutherford worked on the development of hydrophones, to combat the German U-boat menace. His experiments started in the Firth of Forth, where he persuaded a musician to dip his head into the icy water and fix the exact pitch of a submerged submarine's engines.

1919 saw Rutherford back at Cambridge, taking over from Thomson as Professor of Experimental Physics at Cavendish Laboratory and designing the apparatus which first split the atom and released nuclear energy.

Rutherford's work in laying the foundations of nuclear physics was recognised when he was created a baron in 1931, six years before his death. The vast nuclear power stations slowly coming into production today are fitting monuments to this man who opened up a whole exciting new field to the world of science.

THE BOBBY OF BLACK ROCK

BLACK ROCK SURE IS A NICE PEACEFUL TOWN SINCE YOU TOOK OVER, JOE.

IT JUST SHOWS WHAT A FEW BYELAWS CAN DO, MR MAYOR.

JOE CARTER, an English bobby, had become sheriff of the Western township of Black Rock. Joe's boss was the town's mayor.

Just then—

HEY, LOOK AT THE WAY THAT STAGE IS COMIN' INTO TOWN!

I'VE WARNED HIM BEFORE ABOUT SPEEDING! I'LL THROW THE BOOK AT HIM THIS TIME!

JOE, HE AIN'T SPEEDIN'. THAT COACH HAS BEEN ATTACKED BY INJUNS. THEM HORSES IS OUT OF CONTROL!

OUT OF THE WAY, MR MAYOR—I'LL STOP 'EM!

GOTCHA!

COME ON, FELLERS—HELP'S NEEDED HERE!

LOOK AFTER OLD SAM—HE'S HURT REAL BAD!

YOU WERE ONE OF THE PASSENGERS, DAN. WHAT HAPPENED?

CRAZY COOT AN' SOME YOUNG BUCKS ATTACKED US. IT SURE LOOKS LIKE THEM INJUNS ARE ON THE WARPATH!

THIS IS BAD, JOE—WHAT'LL WE DO?

THERE'S GOT TO BE SOME REASON BEHIND IT, MR MAYOR. WE'LL PAY A VISIT TO OLD CHIEF SLY FOX AND FIND OUT.

A few hours later.

THIS IS SOMETHIN' BIG, JOE. THEY'RE WORKIN' THEMSELVES UP FOR A WHOLE HEAP O' TROUBLE!

IT DOESN'T LOOK TOO PROMISING, MR MAYOR. BUT WE MUST TRY TO PUT A STOP TO IT!

HOLD BACK YOUR BRAVES, CHIEF SLY FOX—WE COME IN PEACE!

LET THEM APPROACH! WE CAN TRUST THE ONE IN THE BLUE COAT—HE IS A PEACE-KEEPER FROM FAR-OFF LANDS.

WHY DO YOUR BRAVES DRESS FOR WAR, CHIEF? YOU HAVE SIGNED A PEACE TREATY.

PALEFACE BREAK TREATY—NOW WE BREAK PEACE ARROW AND MAKE WAR ON PALEFACE!

MY SON, CRAZY COOT, FORGETS MANNERS, BUT SPEAKS TRUE. TWO NIGHTS AGO TWO WHITE-EYES CAME HERE AND STOLE OUR SACRED GOLD TOTEM FROM MEDICINE TEPEE.

TELL ME MORE OF THIS, CHIEF.

MEDICINE TEPEE ALWAYS GUARDED, BUT STILL WHITE-EYES GET IN AND STEAL TOTEM!

AND THERE'S HOW THEY GOT IN, CHIEF. THAT'S A TUNNEL THEY'VE DUG—WHAT WE HAVE TO DO IS FIND THE OTHER END!

Within a few minutes the braves were back.

Back in town.

52

IT BELONGED TO A COUPLA FELLERS WHO SAID THEY WERE PROSPECTIN' UP AT THE OLD MINE.

THE OLD MINE —JUST THE PLACE FOR A HIDEOUT! LET'S GO, MR MAYOR!

IT'S ALL BEGINNING TO FIT TOGETHER. THAT TUNNEL WAS DUG BY FELLERS WITH MINING EXPERIENCE. THE THIEVES COULD HAVE BEEN EX-MINERS WHO LEARNED ABOUT THE TOTEM WHILE THEY WORKED THERE!

AND THERE'S A SMELTIN' PLANT UP AT THE MINE, FOR MELTIN' DOWN THE TOTEM!

THERE'S THE WAGON, JOE—NO OTHER SIGN OF LIFE, THOUGH!

THEY CAN'T BE FAR AWAY, MR MAYOR. WE'LL CHECK THE WAGON FIRST—JUST TO BE ON THE SAFE SIDE!

LOOK AT THAT SPLIT RIM—IT'S THE SAME WAGON SURE ENOUGH, JOE!

NO DOUBT OF IT, MR MAYOR. NOW ALL WE HAVE TO FIND IS THE OWNERS. WE'LL TRY THOSE HUTS OVER THERE FIRST!

HOLD IT RIGHT THERE, SHERIFF—YOU TOO, MR MAYOR.

TARNATION! WE'VE WALKED RIGHT INTO A TRAP, JOE!

GET THEIR WEAPONS, CAL, THEN WE'LL TIE 'EM UP!

THE SHERIFF AIN'T GOT NO GUNS. JUST THE MAYOR.

DO YOU FELLERS KNOW WHAT YOU'RE DOING? YOU STOLE THE INDIANS' TOTEM AND UNLESS IT'S RETURNED TO THE INDIANS WITHIN THE NEXT FEW HOURS, THERE'S GOING TO BE WAR!

THAT WON'T BOTHER US, SHERIFF. WE'LL BE LONG GONE BEFORE THAT TIME!

When the men had gone.

WHAT'RE YOU DOIN', JOE?

TRYING TO GET ON MY FEET SO THAT I CAN REACH THAT DESK—THERE MIGHT BE SOMETHING USEFUL IN ONE OF THE DRAWERS!

NICE GOIN', JOE— YOU'RE NEARLY THERE.

I WAS HOP, STEP AND JUMP CHAMPION AT SCHOOL, YOU KNOW!

FIND ANYTHIN', JOE?

HMMM. I'M NOT SURE, MR MAYOR. TRY TO WORK YOUR WAY OVER TO THE WINDOW, WILL YOU?

After five minutes or so—

KEEP STILL, MR MAYOR. THIS MAGNIFYING GLASS WILL DO THE TRICK, BUT I DON'T WANT TO BURN YOU.

NEVER MIND THAT, JOE, IF IT MEANS GETTIN' OUT OF THIS!

IT'S WORKING, MR MAYOR—START PUTTING SOME STRAIN ON THOSE ROPES—

54

55

THE END

A POLICEMAN'S LOT

207

A policeman's job today is a far cry from being just a bobby on the beat.

Added to their work of dealing with crowds and tracking down criminals, police dogs are now being trained to search out narcotics and drugs. Police horses still play a big part in patrolling the larger cities.

Getting to and from accidents in the minimum of time and with maximum efficiency is very important to police motorway patrol units. The motorcycle rider, open to the elements, wears an electric heat-suit generating warmth from his cycle's engine and in the car's boot there's over half a ton of accident equipment.

POLICE

POLICE

58

Air-sea rescue on the River Thames. The Metropolitan Police Force's launches, used mainly to patrol London's vast dockland area, can be used with the force's helicopters. These machines are used for air reconnaissance in conjunction with all the various police forces.

The police also use fast, inflatable, out-board motor dinghies with their frogmen teams as well as for inshore rescue work.

Mountain Rescue. Police teams have saved many lives in the Cairngorm Mountains of Scotland. Skilful training, modern equipment and rough-terrain vehicles help the police teams seek injured or lost climbers in the worst of winters.

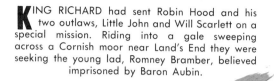

ROBIN HOOD

KING RICHARD had sent Robin Hood and his two outlaws, Little John and Will Scarlett on a special mission. Riding into a gale sweeping across a Cornish moor near Land's End they were seeking the young lad, Romney Bramber, believed imprisoned by Baron Aubin.

WHAT A TERRIBLE PLACE THIS IS, ROBIN! OH, FOR THE SHELTER OF THE GREENWOOD!

I DOUBT IF EVEN OUR SHERWOOD FOREST TREES WOULD AFFORD SHELTER FROM THIS BLAST, LITTLE JOHN.

LOOK, ROBIN! YONDER BUILDING COULD GIVE US SHELTER WHERE WE COULD REST A-WHILE!

A GOODLY IDEA, WILL.

'TIS A STRANGE BUILDING THIS. IT HAS NO DOOR.

METHINKS THE ENTRANCE MUST BE IN THE ROOF. I WILL CLIMB UP YON LADDER AND SEE.

The man drew a knife from his belt.

YOU MONSTER!

ENOUGH TALK! IF YOU WON'T MEET MY DOGS ALIVE, YOU'LL MEET THEM DEAD!

OH NO, YOU DON'T!

AAA-ARRHH!

UGH! HIS DOGS HAVE KILLED HIM!

'TWAS AN ACCIDENT, WILL. I WAS ONLY DEFENDING MYSELF.

THESE BRUTES MUST ALL BE KILLED. IF NOT, NO TRAVELLER WILL EVER SURVIVE ON THIS MOOR.

Robin's deadly arrows wiped out all the hounds. The three travellers waited until the wind died down, then resumed their journey on foot.

62

The sound of a voice shouting from the sea attracted their attention.

HO, THERE, BRAMBER! SHOW YOURSELF SO THAT I KNOW YOU ARE STILL THERE.

IT'S THAT FIEND AUBIN. HE HAS COME TO MOCK ME. ONE OF HIS HIRED KILLERS IS AT THE TILLER.

SO! NOW FOR AUBIN! WITHOUT A HAND ON THE TILLER THAT BOAT WILL RUN AGROUND ON THE STRIP OF BEACH BELOW.

DO NOT TRY TO FREE YOURSELF, BARON AUBIN. IF YOU DO, THE NEXT ARROW WILL GO THROUGH YOUR BLACK HEART.

NOW WE CAN SAFELY ESCAPE FROM YOUR PRISON—IN A BOAT PROVIDED BY BARON AUBIN.

YOU ARE A TRUE FRIEND, ROBIN. NEVER WILL I BE ABLE TO THANK YOU ENOUGH.

TAKE ME WITH YOU! DO NOT LEAVE ME HERE TO DIE!

A TASTE OF YOUR OWN MEDICINE WON'T DO ANY HARM, BARON. YOU CAN STAY THERE UNTIL YOUR MEN COME LOOKING FOR YOU!

Robin picked up Little John and Will.

'TIS WONDERFUL TO BE FREE AGAIN. WHERE SHALL I HEAD FOR, ROBIN?

SAIL EASTWARDS UNTIL MANY MILES ARE BETWEEN US AND BARON AUBIN. WE SHALL RETURN TO SHERWOOD FOREST—YOU SHALL GO TO KING RICHARD. HE WILL SEE THAT AUBIN'S PUNISHED, AND YOU RETURNED TO YOUR RIGHTFUL PLACE!

The End

THE FIRST MOVIE-MAKER

William Friese-Greene was one of the great pioneers of photography. In 1877, aged 22, he owned successful portrait studios in Bath and Plymouth, as well as his native Bristol.

John Rudge showed him his "Biophantic Lantern", which projected a quick succession of coloured drawings making a clown appear to turn a somersault. Friese-Greene realised that the same idea could be applied to photography.

Improving on Rudge's lantern design, Friese-Greene projected a series of photographs showing his own face change from a frown to a smile. An old lady attacked the screen with her umbrella.

Friese-Greene moved to London. To publicise his invention, he projected a moving picture of a dancing skeleton on a screen across his studio window. A huge crowd formed and the police asked him to stop.

In January 1889 he shot his first film with his first cine-camera, the famous "Magic Box". Instead of the usual cumbersome glass plates, it used the new type of celluloid film produced by Friese-Greene himself.

He worked into the night to develop and print the film. A surprised policeman, dragged into the studio by the excited movie-maker, became the world's first motion-picture audience.

In 1904, "The Great Train Robbery", a 12-minute Western film, was the talk of London. One sequence, when a railway engine appeared to be charging straight out of the screen, usually caused panic in the audience. Friese-Greene, having sold the patent of his invention to pay for further experiments, died penniless in 1921.

Suddenly.

LOOK, A SIGNAL OF DISTRESS FROM THE SEA.

A SHIP COULD EASILY MEET TROUBLE WITH THE ICE CLOSING IN. TODD AND I WILL INVESTIGATE.

GIVE ME A RIDE, TEACHER. WE MUST GET THERE QUICKLY.

TWO AMERICAN SAILORS, ATTACKED BY A POLAR BEAR. TO THE RESCUE, TEACHER!

HELP!

JEEPERS! A— A ROBOT!

DO NOT BE ALARMED. I WILL DEAL WITH THE BEAR.

I-IT'S THROWING THE BEAR AROUND LIKE IT WAS A KITTEN!

THAT BEAR AIN'T COMING BACK FOR MORE!

I'M JAKE TODD, AND THAT IS THE IRON TEACHER. WHY ARE YOU HERE? YOU'RE NOT DRESSED FOR ARCTIC WEATHER.

WE WERE CLIMBING THAT RIDGE TO LOOK FOR A SETTLEMENT WHEN WE DISTURBED THE BEAR. WE'VE BEEN MAROONED! THE REST OF OUR PARTY IS OVER THERE.

THERE'S OUR DESTROYER, A SCIENTIFIC SURVEY SHIP. SOME OF THE CREW MUTINIED. WE MANAGED TO GET OFF A DISTRESS ROCKET BEFORE WE WERE DUMPED ON THE ICE.

THE LEADER OF THE MUTINEERS IS AL ROCCO. HE'S AN OUT AND OUT PIRATE. HE'LL CAUSE HAVOC ON THE SHIPPING LANES.

THEY CANNOT MOVE FAST THROUGH THE ICE FLOES. TODD AND I WILL GO AFTER THEM. I WILL DIRECT YOU TO THE ESKIMO SETTLEMENT FOR SHELTER.

ONE MAN AND A METAL CONTRAPTION AGAINST A DESTROYER!

YOU SHOULD HAVE SEEN THAT ROBOT HANDLE A BEAR, SIR!

THE ICE IS THICKENING AHEAD OF THE DESTROYER. THEY WON'T GET MUCH FURTHER.

THE ICE IS SOLID UP AHEAD! THE BOWS WILL CAVE IN IF WE GO ON, ROCCO.

REVERSE ENGINES!

THE ICE HAS CLOSED IN ALL ROUND THEM. THEY'RE TRAPPED! COME ON, TEACHER.

YOU CANNOT ESCAPE! YOU ARE TRAPPED HERE UNTIL THE U.S. NAVY ARRIVES. SURRENDER NOW, AND SAVE YOUR LIVES.

GEE, WHAT'S THAT THING?

A MACHINE-GUN! BUT THE BULLETS WON'T HARM YOU, TEACHER.

THE BULLETS ARE JUST BOUNCING OFF THAT METAL MAN!

WE'LL USE THE THREE-INCH GUN!

THEY'RE TURNING THE BIG STUFF ON US! BETTER GET OUT OF HERE, TEACHER!

THE LITTLE GUY'S DOWN, AND THAT METAL MAN AIN'T MOVING.

GET 'EM BOTH ABOARD. I CAN USE A METAL MAN THAT AIN'T HARMED BY MACHINE-GUN BULLETS.

THIS GUY'S COMING ROUND. BUT THERE AIN'T NO SIGN OF LIFE IN THE ROBOT.

I GUESS THIS GUY KNOWS HOW TO GET IT GOING—AND HE'LL SOON TALK.

HOW DO I MAKE THAT THING WORK?

THE CONTROL PANEL IS INSIDE MY GLOVE, BUT I'M NOT TELLING THEM THAT!

TALK!

UH!

YOUR METAL PAL WON'T STAND UP TO A SHELL AT POINT-BLANK RANGE, BUDDY! SO TALK!

TIME FOR THE IRON TEACHER TO GO INTO ACTION.

THE METAL MAN'S COME TO LIFE!

GEE, HE'S TWISTING THE GUN BARREL!

HE'S COMING FOR US! WE CAN'T STOP HIM!

Jake thought quickly.

KEEP OFF, IRON MAN, OR YOUR PAL GETS IT!

HE'S TURNING AWAY!

WHERE'S HE GOING?

HE'S JUMPED! HE'S GOING CLEAN THROUGH THE ICE!

HE'S GONE UNDER! THAT'S THE END OF HIM! WE'LL SOON FIX THIS OTHER GUY!

I'VE SWITCHED ON THE TEACHER'S MAGNETIC HAND!

Under water the Iron Teacher clung to the hull of the destroyer with one magnetic hand.

On deck.

WHAT'S THAT NOISE? SOMETHING'S HAMMERING THE HULL.

I BET IT'S THE IRON MAN AGAIN!

The Teacher's mighty strength punched a hole in the hull of the ship.

ROCCO, THE SHIP'S HOLED! WATER'S POURING IN!

NOW'S MY CHANCE!

STOP THAT GUY!

GET HIM!

NEVER MIND HIM, ROCCO! THE SHIP'S SINKING!

THE END

A Page Of Pirates

CAPTAIN CHARLES GIBBS—was like Al Rocco, the pirate brought to book by the Iron Teacher. Serving aboard the American ship, Vineyard, Gibbs led a mutiny. He captured a vast treasure hidden below the deck-planking and, seizing the ship, became a pirate. But when, later, some of the Vineyard's loyal crewmen escaped, Gibbs was captured and hanged.

BLACKBEARD—was perhaps the most notorious and feared of all the pirates. Captain Edward Teach, a huge man with an enormous black beard, came from Bristol. He went into action, armed with three pairs of pistols and a spinechilling assortment of swords and knives. But what really scared his victims were the burning fuses which he stuck under the brim of his hat.

BATHOLOMEW ROBERTS— a Welsh pirate who always liked to be well dressed, seized over 400 ships. He also captured the fort on the Island of Princes, off the African coast and threw its guns into the sea. Resplendent in rich, red damask clothes and a peacock feather hat, Roberts finally met his end at the hands of Captain Ogle of the warship, Swallow.

CAPTAIN JOHN PHILLIPS, an English ship's carpenter, was working in the New-foundland fish docks when he and a few others seized a ship and sailed as pirates. Proud of his trade, he made his men swear allegiance to him on the head of his carpenter's axe. By a strange twist of fate, he was killed when prisoners he had taken seized his carpenter's tools and attacked him with them.

COWARDY CUSTER

'TIS CHRISTMAS EVE, TWITCH. I NEED SOMEONE TO—

THERE HE GOES, VOLUNTEERING AGAIN. WELL, I'M OFF!

CUSTER was the battle-charger of the renowned Cavalier, Sir Waldo Twitch. But, unknown to his master, Custer had a mind of his own and a knack for avoiding personal danger.

SAY NO MORE, M'LORD. I'M YOUR MAN!

MY HORSE! WHERE BE MY NOBLE CHARGER?

YONDER, SIR WALDO. I'LL GET HIM!

ROTTEN TELL TALE. I'LL GET HIM FOR THAT!

YOU ARE FRISKY TODAY, GALLANT STEED.

AAGH!

THAT'S US QUITS!

'TIS AN ERRAND OF PEACE WE ARE BOUND ON, CUSTER.

GOOD! I DON'T LIKE FIGHTING. I'M A NATURAL COWARD!

Later.

YONDER BE THE SLED, YOUR HONOUR. I WILL TAKE YOU INSIDE TO SEE MY MASTERPIECE.

SLED? WHAT'S ALL THIS ABOUT?

CHARLIE'S ANT

Charlie Smith had an ant as a pal and the ant, of course, was very strong.

THE END

OUT of the Antarctic ice rears a huge, fearsome monster and the men working at the vast natural frozen food storage depot flee in terror.

THE SCARLET HAWK

Suddenly.

IT'S COMING FOR US! WATCH OUT, HAWK!

ROCKETS ON!

I HIT IT, BUT THE MISSILES GLANCED OFF ITS HIDE. NOW THE LIGHT'S SCARED IT OFF!

LOOK OUT! THE ROCKETS HAVE BROUGHT DOWN THE ROOF!

WE'RE TRAPPED!

NOT TO WORRY! WE'LL MELT OUR WAY OUT WITH THE LASER, STROGO!

Meanwhile.

SIGNAL JUST COME IN, SIR. THE MONSTER WAS LAST SEEN TAKING TO THE WATER.

HEAR THAT, EVERYONE? KEEP YOUR EYES PEELED!

STARBOARD TEN DEGREES! STAND BY, TORPEDOES! STAND BY, GUN CREW! FIRE WHEN READY!

87

THE BLACK SAPPER

THE Black Sapper arrived in California in answer to a call for help from the local police. In his amazing machine, the Worm, he emerged from the ground near the harbour of San Francisco.

AN UNDERWATER ERUPTION! YOU'RE JUST IN TIME TO WITNESS IT, SAPPER.

MY INSTRUMENTS RECORDED UNUSUAL ACTIVITY IN THIS AREA, PROFESSOR JOHNSON. LOOK! IT'S CAUGHT THAT FISHING BOAT!

THE COASTGUARDS WILL GET ANY SURVIVORS. THIS IS A VOLCANIC AREA AND WITH ACTIVITY INCREASING, YOU MAY BE IN FOR A MAJOR EARTHQUAKE, PROFESSOR.

THAT'S WHAT WE FEAR. SAN FRANCISCO WAS FLATTENED BY AN EARTHQUAKE IN 1906. NOW WE'RE GETTING A SERIES OF MINOR DISTURBANCES. BUT THEY DON'T SEEM TO FOLLOW ANY PATTERN.

WE'VE MARKED THE SITES OF THE DISTURBANCES, AND WE'RE HOPING YOU'LL INVESTIGATE—

WAIT! LOOK AT THE GOLDEN GATE BRIDGE! IT'S COLLAPSING!

The great bridge crashed down.

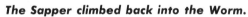

The Sapper climbed back into the Worm.

IT MUST HAVE BEEN AN EARTH SHIFT, RIGHT UNDER THE TOWER OF THE BRIDGE. THIS IS TERRIBLE.

THE SAPPER'S HEADING FOR THE SPOT.

The Worm bored though the ground towards the base of the bridge.

MY INSTRUMENTS RECORD NUCLEAR RADIATION AROUND THE FOUNDATIONS OF THE BRIDGE! I'M SHIELDED FROM IT IN THE WORM.

The Sapper had towed the bomb to the outskirts of the city, but the shock was felt on the surface.

THE EARTH'S SPLITTING!

IT'S AN EARTHQUAKE!

AAGH!

THE WORM WITHSTOOD THE BLAST. EVERYTHING STILL WORKS, AND I GOT THE BOMB CLEAR OF THE SAN ANDREAS FAULT IN TIME. NOW I HAVE TO FIND THE MADMAN WHO PLANTED IT.

HE MUST BE NEAR, BUT HE'D WANT TO BE SAFE FROM THE EARTHQUAKE. AH, THERE'S A HUGE HELICOPTER CIRCLING ABOVE. COULD HE BE IN THAT? I'LL SURFACE.

THE BLACK SAPPER'S WORM IS SURFACING BELOW! IT SURVIVED THAT BOMB!

THE SAPPER'S WRECKED MY PLANS! HE'LL PAY FOR THIS. WE HAVE ONE SMALL ATOMIC BOMB LEFT. TELL THE PILOT TO TAKE US DOWN.

KING OF THE WHIP

HARRY NETHERFIELD was the son of a poor Australian homesteader. At the age of fifteen he was doing a man's work on his father's outback farm. Then, one day in 1855, something happened that changed his whole life.

HARRY, BETTER SADDLE A HORSE AND GO AND FLUSH THE STOCK OUT OF THE RIVER BED. IF THIS RAIN KEEPS ON, WE'RE LIKELY TO HAVE TROUBLE.

YE'RE RIGHT, PA. A FLASH FLOOD COULD DROWN THE LOT!

WATCH OUT, HARRY. SOME OF THEM YOUNG BULLS WON'T LIKE BEING CHASED OUT OF THE SHELTER OF THE SCRUB.

DON'T WORRY, PA, I'VE GOT MY STOCK-WHIP.

CATTLE HAVE NO SENSE. YOU DON'T FIND HORSES SHELTERING WHERE THEY'RE LIABLE TO GET DROWNED!

There was no danger when Harry reached the dried-up Cocklebiddy River, but he knew that, in a few hours—perhaps less—the river bed could become a raging torrent. So—

HI-HI-HI! GERROUT OF IT, YER STUPID GALAHS!

G'DAY, YOU-FELLER COLBUNG. YER RECKON BIG-WATER COMING?

YOU BETCHA, BIG WATER COME. FILL HIM RIVER. WASH AWAY HIM HUMPY-ON-WHEELS!

HUMPY-ON-WHEELS? GO ON! THERE AIN'T NO CARRIAGES IN THESE PARTS! YOU MEAN A WAGON.

ME TELL STRAIGHT, BOSS. HIM BY BRIDGE BELONG BARDI CREEK. NOT WAGON—HIM HUMPY-ON-WHEELS.

But they weren't newcomers camping. A Cobb & Co. stage-coach had become bogged down in the creek!

I'D BETTER LOOK INTO THIS. IF THERE REALLY IS SOMEBODY CAMPED BY BARDI CREEK THEY MUST BE NEWCOMERS—A DINKUM AUSSIE WOULD HAVE MORE SENSE!

STONE THE CROWS! THEY MUST BE OPENING UP A NEW ROUTE THROUGH HERE.

Camping in a dry river bed was asking for trouble. Many Australian rivers had no water in them for years. But heavy rain could bring on a flash flood—a great wall of water which surged down the river bed, sweeping everything before it.

YER COULD USE AN EXTRA PULL, MATE. GET A ROPE AND I'LL GIVE IT A GO.

GOOD ON YER, SPORT.

BIG-WATER COMING! YOU MAKE QUICK ALONG HUMPY-ON-WHEELS!

IT'S A FLASH FLOOD! WE'LL NEVER MAKE IT!

THIS IS TERRIBLE! HE ISN'T GOING TO—?

NO, HE WON'T DIE, MISTER COBB. BUT HE'S GOING TO BE AWFUL SICK FOR A FEW DAYS.

THIS IS GONNA SET MY BUSINESS BACK BADLY—ALL THESE PASSENGERS STRANDED.

WE CAN FIND SOME ROOM FOR 'EM UNTIL YER CAN GET ANOTHER DRIVER OUT.

NO NEED FOR THAT, PA. I'LL TAKE THE COACH ON, IF MISTER COBB WILL GIVE ME THE CHANCE!

YOU'D NEVER HANDLE THE LEVIATHAN'S TEAM, SON!

HOW D'YER KNOW? I'M GOOD WITH HORSES. ANYWAY, IT'S FOR MISTER COBB TO DECIDE!

I'M GONNA TAKE A CHANCE. WE PULL OUT ACCORDING TO SCHEDULE WITH HARRY NETHERFIELD ON THE BOX!

THEY'RE GONNA TAKE SOME HOLDING, LAD, AND THE REINS ARE ONLY MAKESHIFT, YER KNOW. THEY WAS ONLY MADE FOR A SIX-HORSE TEAM.

I KNOW, PA—BUT I CAN HANDLE 'EM WITHOUT REINS, IF I HAVE TO!

Nothing as big as the Leviathan had been seen on the Australian roads up to that time.

LOOK AT THAT NEW COACH OF COBB'S! IT'S AS BIG AS A BATTLESHIP!

AND LOOK WHO'S ON THE BOX. IT'S YOUNG HARRY NETHERFIELD.

But later came trouble!

A BUNCH OF 'ROOS! THEY'VE SCARED THE HORSES. WHOA!

And on the heels of trouble came disaster. The makeshift reins snapped under the strain!

103

KING of the WHIP

A COACH RACE GAME FOR ANY NUMBER OF PLAYERS

All you need:—A small shirt button for each player as a counter, a cup and a dice.

RULES:—You must throw a six to start. You must get exactly the number required to land at the finishing post. You cannot enter an occupied square. Stop behind it if your throw would result in sharing it. You CAN overtake, unless barred from doing so.

START

FINISH

SHORT CUT

NEW BRIDGE. GO ON 3 PLACES

FRESH HORSES. GO ON 4 PLACES.

HORSE LAME. MISS 1 THROW.

DETOUR.

TREE ACROSS TRAIL. TAKE DETOUR.

TRAIL FLOODED. MUST THROW 3 TO GO ON.

HELD UP! GO BACK TO POST.

DRY WATER HOLE. GO BACK TO POST.

BROKEN WHEEL. MISS 1 THROW.

FRESH HORSES. GO ON 4 PLACES.

STAGING POST

FRESH HORSES. GO ON 4 PLACES.

NO OVERTAKING. NARROW GORGE.

LONELY LARRY

LONELY LARRY, who had been a castaway since he was a child, lived on a remote South Sea island. His only companion was Tommy, his pet toucan.

WEAPONS OF WORLD WAR TWO

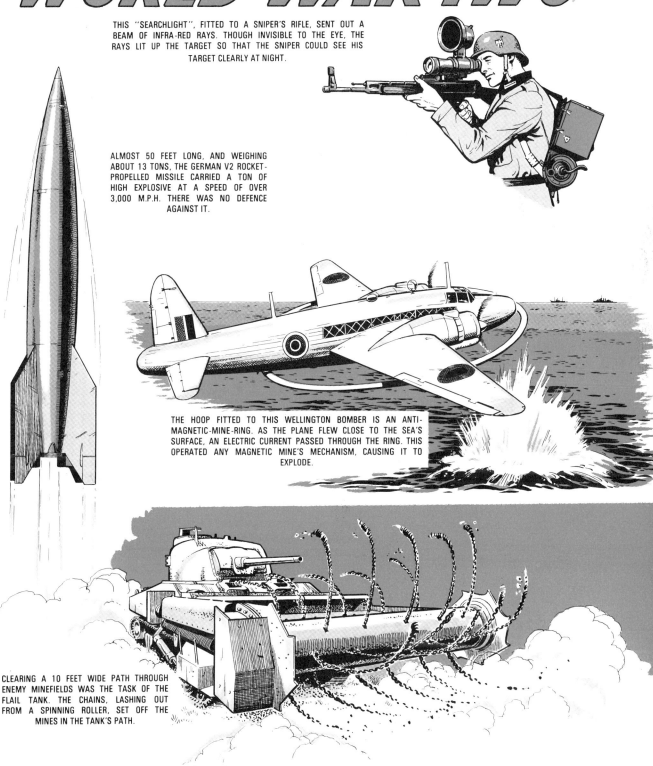

THIS "SEARCHLIGHT", FITTED TO A SNIPER'S RIFLE, SENT OUT A BEAM OF INFRA-RED RAYS. THOUGH INVISIBLE TO THE EYE, THE RAYS LIT UP THE TARGET SO THAT THE SNIPER COULD SEE HIS TARGET CLEARLY AT NIGHT.

ALMOST 50 FEET LONG, AND WEIGHING ABOUT 13 TONS, THE GERMAN V2 ROCKET-PROPELLED MISSILE CARRIED A TON OF HIGH EXPLOSIVE AT A SPEED OF OVER 3,000 M.P.H. THERE WAS NO DEFENCE AGAINST IT.

THE HOOP FITTED TO THIS WELLINGTON BOMBER IS AN ANTI-MAGNETIC-MINE-RING. AS THE PLANE FLEW CLOSE TO THE SEA'S SURFACE, AN ELECTRIC CURRENT PASSED THROUGH THE RING. THIS OPERATED ANY MAGNETIC MINE'S MECHANISM, CAUSING IT TO EXPLODE.

CLEARING A 10 FEET WIDE PATH THROUGH ENEMY MINEFIELDS WAS THE TASK OF THE FLAIL TANK. THE CHAINS, LASHING OUT FROM A SPINNING ROLLER, SET OFF THE MINES IN THE TANK'S PATH.

WEAPONS
OF WORLD WAR TWO (CONTINUED)

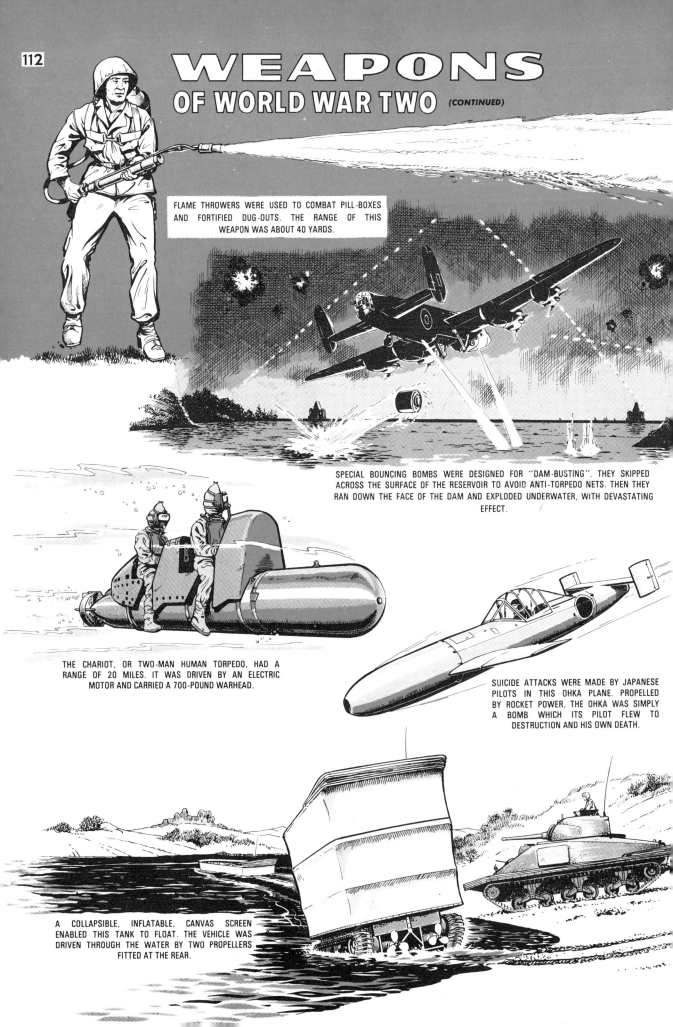

FLAME THROWERS WERE USED TO COMBAT PILL-BOXES AND FORTIFIED DUG-OUTS. THE RANGE OF THIS WEAPON WAS ABOUT 40 YARDS.

SPECIAL BOUNCING BOMBS WERE DESIGNED FOR "DAM-BUSTING". THEY SKIPPED ACROSS THE SURFACE OF THE RESERVOIR TO AVOID ANTI-TORPEDO NETS. THEN THEY RAN DOWN THE FACE OF THE DAM AND EXPLODED UNDERWATER, WITH DEVASTATING EFFECT.

THE CHARIOT, OR TWO-MAN HUMAN TORPEDO, HAD A RANGE OF 20 MILES. IT WAS DRIVEN BY AN ELECTRIC MOTOR AND CARRIED A 700-POUND WARHEAD.

SUICIDE ATTACKS WERE MADE BY JAPANESE PILOTS IN THIS OHKA PLANE. PROPELLED BY ROCKET POWER, THE OHKA WAS SIMPLY A BOMB WHICH ITS PILOT FLEW TO DESTRUCTION AND HIS OWN DEATH.

A COLLAPSIBLE, INFLATABLE, CANVAS SCREEN ENABLED THIS TANK TO FLOAT. THE VEHICLE WAS DRIVEN THROUGH THE WATER BY TWO PROPELLERS FITTED AT THE REAR.

THREE AGAINST THE LION

TOSHIRO, a young Japanese boy, is helpless as Kenji a samurai, puts him across his knee—and smacks him!

114

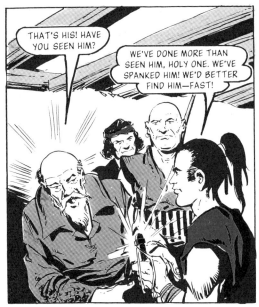

THAT'S HIS! HAVE YOU SEEN HIM?

WE'VE DONE MORE THAN SEEN HIM, HOLY ONE. WE'VE SPANKED HIM! WE'D BETTER FIND HIM—FAST!

In a village some miles from the monastery—

YOU WANT FOOD AND A ROOM FOR THE NIGHT! HA! HA! AND HOW WILL YOU PAY FOR IT, YOU LITTLE TRAMP?

FOOL! MY FATHER IS THE DAIMYO OF NAGATO. I DRESS SO TO AVOID BEING TAKEN BY ROBBERS AND BANDITS!

HEAR THAT? THAT'S THE BOY WE'RE AFTER! IT'S LUCKY WE DECIDED TO STOP AT THIS INN TO EAT.

THE LION WILL BE PLEASED WITH US. LET THE BOY SETTLE INTO HIS ROOM, AND THEN—

And at another village not far away—

NO SIGN OF HIM HERE. LET'S TRY THE NEXT VILLAGE. I CAN'T SEE THAT BOY SLEEPING ROUGH.

At the next village—

LET'S ASK IN HERE. THESE LOOK LIKE HORSES BELONGING TO A WAR-LORD'S GUARD. RECOGNIZE THE SADDLE CRESTS, EITHER OF YOU?

NOT ME.

THE INN-KEEPER! HE'S DEAD!

IT MUST BE THOSE WARRIORS. AND THEY'RE STILL HERE.

Then—

LOOK! OVER THERE! GET THEM!

TAKE THE BOY OUT THE WINDOW! WE'LL DEAL WITH THESE STRANGERS.

117

WHEN SAMURAI HELD SWAY

The great tradition of the samurai, the professional soldier of Japan, lasted nearly 500 years. The coming of the musket in the middle of the 16th century wiped out the samurai, whose bushido, code of honour, was based on single combat.

A ten-foot spear and two swords were carried by the foot soldier.

An archer whose armour was lacquered leather strips.

A Japanese musketeer of the 1580's.

A fully armoured samurai was a fearsome sight.

The armoured cavalry-man was also a mounted archer.

OSSIE

THE OUTLAW

The first British troop-carrying glider to be produced was the General Aircraft Limited "Hotspur". A dual-control training glider, it was used in the preparations for the airborne landings in Normandy and at Arnhem, during the Second World War. Realistic explosions as the gliders landed on exercises hardened the airborne troops for the battles which lay ahead.

Few football clubs can rival the brilliant record of Tottenham Hotspur F.C., whose ground is at White Hart Lane, London. The club was formed in 1882 by a group of local boys. The Percy family owned large estates in Tottenham, and the boys' imagination had been fired by the story of Harry Hotspur, which is how they came to choose the name.

Popularly known as the "Spurs", the club turned professional in 1895. Since then, Tottenham Hotspur have won the F.A. Cup five times and the Football League Championship twice, including the "Double" in 1961, the European Cup-Winners' Cup, the U.E.F.A. Cup and the Football League Cup twice. No one can say the Spurs haven't added lustre to the Percy name!